The Prosecution of
Peter Pumpkin-Eater

The Prosecution of Peter Pumpkin-Eater

Peter Hunt

The Federation Press
1998

Published in Sydney by:
  The Federation Press
  PO Box 45, Annandale, NSW, 2038.
  71 John St, Leichhardt, NSW, 2040.
  Ph (02) 9552 2200. Fax (02) 9552 1681.

National Library of Australia
Cataloguing-in-Publication entry:

  Hunt, Peter (Peter John).
  The prosecution of Peter Pumpkin-Eater

  ISBN 1 86287 289 9.

  1. Criminal procedure – Australia. I. Title.

345.9405

Typeset by The Federation Press, Leichhardt, NSW.
    Printed by Southwood Press, Marrickville, NSW.

Contents

For Boh, my darling wife and huckleberry friend.

The Police Interview

Poor Peter Pumpkin-Eater sat sadly in a sad room all alone.

He felt sorrow when he thought that he was all by himself. He felt even more sorrow when he considered his plight. After all, he was in a police station. And furthermore, those grumpy policemen who brought him there did not seem at all happy with him.

Peter Pumpkin-Eater looked around the sad room. After thinking for a while he decided that it needed a good coat of paint. The sad grey colour was entirely too sad to contemplate. A rich orange colour would be far better. Yes, the colour of a pumpkin would be far happier than the sad grey colour. That was more like the colour of angry storm clouds.

As Peter thought about the colour of the room the door opened. Peter looked up quickly. He frowned as two policemen dressed all in blue strode in.

"Only angry men stride that way", Peter thought to himself.

The two policemen frowned in Peter's direction as they sat on chairs on the opposite side of the table to him. The first policeman looked at

Peter and then at the second policeman and shook his round head. Meanwhile, the second policeman looked at the wall behind Peter. When he noticed the first policeman looking at him he looked back, saw the round head shaking, and then looked at Peter and shook his round head too. Peter was confused by this behaviour. He decided to shake his head as well. However, his head was both bigger and rounder than either the first policeman or the second policeman. After all, he did eat a lot of pumpkins! When the first policeman saw this he stopped shaking his head and wagged his chin instead.

"Mr Pumpkin-Eater, my name is Inspector Nightstick and this is Constable Illot. We have asked you to accompany us here today to assist in our enquiries regarding a complaint made by Mrs Pumpkin-Eater. Do you understand?"

Peter swallowed hard. Inspector Nightstick had a very deep voice which impressed Peter. It was a voice which, in some way Peter did not understand, commanded respect and obedience. Peter nodded his head and replied that he understood.

"Good, now I must make it clear, Mr Pumpkin-Eater, that you do not have to talk to me today. You have that right. However, anything you do say to me may be used against you in a court of law."

Peter swallowed again and said solemnly, "Gosh."

"Do you understand your rights Mr Pumpkin-Eater?"

Peter swallowed a third time and replied, "Yes, I understand."

"Mr Pumpkin-Eater, are you happy to talk to me today about this matter?"

Peter Pumpkin-Eater thought for a long time about this question. Eventually he said that although he was not happy about the colour of the walls he was happy to talk to the policemen.

"Good. Now, Mr Pumpkin-Eater, your wife has made some serious allegations. You are, of course, well known to us . . . and only in the best of ways. Even my youngest boy knows of you. His name is Peter as well and it seems that his friends call him 'Pumpkin-Eater' all the time. In any event, I must perform my duty, unhappy though that duty may be. I am going to ask you some questions and Constable Illot here is going to record those questions and your answers in his notebook. Do you understand?"

"Yes."

"Fine. Now . . . can you tell me the current whereabouts of Mrs Pumpkin-Eater?"

Inspector Nightstick looked sternly at Peter. Peter, in return, held his gaze before looking away. He then whispered, "Why, she's at home."

"Now Mr Pumpkin-Eater, when you say 'at home' you mean, I take it, your residence, 'Pumpkin Shell Cottage'."

"I don't understand the question", Peter said tilting his head.

"Peter . . . is it the words I am using which you don't understand or is it that you do not understand the information I am seeking?"

"Neither. I simply do not understand why you ask the question. You know where I live."

As Peter Pumpkin-Eater said these words both Inspector Nightstick and Constable Illot shook their round heads and then turned to each other. Then, simultaneously, they leaned forward in their chairs and looked earnestly at Peter. After a long time Inspector Nightstick said slowly, "Mr Pumpkin-Eater, we do know where you live. We also know where Mrs Pumpkin-Eater lives. The problem is that she appears to have lived there for some considerable time . . ."

"Well she is my wife. She is, as you say, Mrs Pumpkin-Eater."

"Peter, our information is that your wife has not eaten pumpkin for quite some time . . ."

Looking baffled, Peter exclaimed, "What has that got to do with it? So what if she has not eaten pumpkin for years. She doesn't like pumpkin. So what?"

The silence that followed was broken by Constable Illot's bewildered whisper, "How can she be called Mrs Pumpkin-Eater if she does not eat pumpkin?"

Inspector Nightstick's response to Constable Illot's query was to laugh in astonishment. Realising the humour of it, Constable Illot laughed as well. The only ones not laughing were Peter Pumpkin-Eater and the grey walls around him.

When they had finished laughing, Inspector Nightstick looked at Peter. Realising the seriousness of the matter, he looked away from Peter and said, "Mr Pumpkin-Eater, I apologise. We should not be laughing in these circumstances. Allow me to ask you this question . . . how long has it been since Mrs Pumpkin-Eater, if I may call her that, has left 'Pumpkin Shell Cottage'?"

"How long since she left 'Pumpkin Shell Cottage'?"

"Yes, how long?"

"I'm sorry, I do not understand why this is important to you."

At this Inspector Nightstick, hit the table with the palm of his hand. He stood up and paced around the sad, grey room. After about a minute, Constable Illot realised that he too should be pacing around the room. So he slammed the table with his closed fist as well and stood up. He proceeded to walk purposefully around the room behind Inspector Nightstick. Then the latter stopped suddenly, causing Constable Illot to run into the back of him, before sitting down again. After a long time, Inspector Nightstick said, "You are causing me concern Mr Pumpkin-Eater. You have asked me why it is important for me to know how long it has been since your non-pumpkin eating wife, Mrs Pumpkin-Eater, has left 'Pumpkin Shell Cottage'. The answer,

Mr Pumpkin-Eater relates to the allegations Mrs Pumpkin-Eater has made against you . . ."

"What are those . . . ?"

"Mrs Pumpkin-Eater has, I regret to say Mr Pumpkin-Eater, accused you of falsely imprisoning her in 'Pumpkin Shell Cottage' . . ."

"But there I kept her very well!"

"That may be so, Mr Pumpkin-Eater! That may very well be so! But that is not the point. The point is that it is a criminal offence to keep somebody against their will. You're not allowed to do that . . ."

"Who says?"

"Society, Mr Pumpkin-Eater, society says so! And failing that, the government says so!"

Upon hearing these words Peter Pumpkin-Eater rolled his eyes and said, "And since when do you care what society or the government says?"

"That's it Mr Pumpkin-Eater! I demand an answer. How long has it been since your wife, the good Mrs Pumpkin-Eater, left 'Pumpkin-Shell Cottage'?"

Peter Pumpkin-Eater closed his eyes and thought. He thought for a long time. When he opened them again he had come to a decision. He leaned forward in his chair and stated simply, "I do not wish to answer any further questions until I have consulted a lawyer."

Inspector Nightstick and Constable Illot both fell back in their chairs. It was as if the very force of

I demand an answer.

Peter's words had pushed them backwards. At the same time, each policeman let out a puff of air. Finally, Inspector Nightstick said, "All right then. We will have to let you go for now. But first I am charging you, Peter Pumpkin-Eater, with the offence of unlawful imprisonment. The matter will go before the court in two days time. I suggest you see a lawyer before then."

"But who should I see? Who is a good lawyer?"

Inspector Nightstick merely smiled in response to Peter's question before getting up and leaving the sad, grey room. Constable Illot smiled a similar smile before also getting up to leave. However, before he left, Constable Illot whispered, "Mollie Mouthpiece. She's a good lawyer. Go and see her."

The Solicitor's Office

"**A**ll right Sir, please take a seat. It is a wonderful day outside isn't it. Now, how can I help you?"

Peter Pumpkin-Eater walked cautiously into his solicitor's office. As he did so he gasped. The office was painted dark green. The colour of pumpkin leaves. Very soothing. However, it was more than the colour of the walls which impressed him. Along each of the walls were shelves and shelves of books. Some of the books were burgundy in colour with mustard coloured labels. Others were mustard in colour with burgundy coloured labels. Others still were vanilla in colour with chocolate coloured labels. All these colours made Peter hungry just to look at them. He was therefore amused when he saw some of the books had the word "Digest" written on them.

As he looked at all of the books Peter Pumpkin-Eater thought to himself, "I have come to the right place. Look at all of these books. This lady must know an awful lot!"

Peter sat down in the seat Mollie Mouthpiece was pointing to. He then remembered the question she had asked and said, "Oh, I am in trouble with the police. I'm not sure what it is about. Something about my wife and keeping her at home . . ."

Mollie Mouthpiece looked blankly at Peter Pumpkin-Eater and said, "What on earth is wrong with that?"

"I don't know. It is all very confusing."

"Well, did you bring any papers with you?"

"Papers?"

"Yes, papers from the police indicating the charges being brought against you."

"Oh . . . no . . . I didn't bring them. They are at home. Sorry."

"Well they're not doing much good at home now are they? Do you recall the name of the police officer who charged you?"

"Yes, Inspector Nightstick."

"All right. Just a moment."

Mollie Mouthpiece then picked up her telephone. She shook her head dramatically so that her mousy blonde hair bounced behind her ear. Her fingers danced over the buttons on the phone. Then she spoke, "Oh, Nigel! Hello, Mollie Mouthpiece, Solicitor, here. How are you? Good. Now, I have Peter Pumpkin-Eater here with me in my office. He says that you brought him in yesterday and had a chat with him. Charged him I think. Something to do with his wife . . . right . . . yes . . . I see . . . imprisoned her did he . . . how so . . . kept her in the house . . . right. You're serious about this one I take it. All right. Thank you Nigel. I'll get instructions. Good."

Mollie Mouthpiece quietly made some notes on her yellow pad whilst Peter Pumpkin-Eater watched in silence. He was uncomfortable, not knowing what to do or what to say. Peter was relieved when Mollie Mouthpiece's small mouth opened again and words came out.

"Well, as you have heard, I've spoken to Inspector Nightstick. It seems that the charge against you is that you have unlawfully imprisoned your wife, Mrs Pumpkin-Eater. The particulars of that charge are that you caused your wife to be imprisoned within your own home. Now, I need to get your instructions on that charge. What do you say?

Peter thought for a while before saying, "I'm not sure what you mean. What do you want me to say?"

With a little sigh, her eyes sparkling behind her round spectacles, Mollie Mouthpiece rephrased her question, "The police, Mr Pumpkin-Eater, say that you have unlawfully imprisoned your wife in your house. That is, you have prevented her from leaving your home. Do you agree with the police that you have done this or do your disagree that you have done this?"

"Is everything I say here a secret, Miss Mouthpiece?"

"That's Ms Mouthpiece thank you. And yes, everything you say to me is a secret. I am not allowed to repeat what you tell me without your permission."

"What if I told you that the police are right?"

"Then that would be our secret. However, I would have to advise you to plead guilty to the charge against you. If you rejected my advice and decided to plead not guilty then I would tell you that I could no longer act for you."

"I am sorry but I do not understand. Why wouldn't you act for me?"

"I would not be able to act for you, Mr Pumpkin-Eater, because even though I have a duty to keep your secrets, I also have a duty not to mislead the court. If you told me you were guilty I could not then mislead the court by arguing that you were not guilty. So, my only option would be to refuse to act for you. That way, I neither give away your secret nor mislead the court."

"But, Ms Mouthpiece, if I was guilty I would learn my lesson and lie to my next solicitor by saying that I was not guilty."

"NMP."

"NMP?"

"Not my problem."

"Not your problem? Not your problem! How can it not be your problem when you have refused to help somebody who needs your help?"

"Mr Pumpkin-Eater. It is not my job to assist a person who I know to be guilty. If a client tells me he is guilty he must either accept my advice that he plead guilty or find a new solicitor . . ."

"Ms Mouthpiece. What if you know your client is guilty even though he has not told you he is guilty?"

"What?"

"I asked you what you would do if you knew that your client was guilty through some other means than him telling you so."

"It's not my job to judge my client, Mr Pumpkin-Eater."

"What do you mean?"

"I simply mean that it is not part of my brief to weigh up all the facts I know about your matter and apportion guilt. All I have to do is promote your interests. The way I do that is to listen to what you have to say, believe what you tell me unless it is totally unbelievable, and present your case to the court with the thought in mind that your version is the absolute truth. I must ensure that your version prevails."

"But I don't understand the difference."

"The difference between what?"

"I don't understand why you would not judge me if you knew some fact about my case which proved beyond doubt that I was guilty when you would judge me if I told you I was guilty."

"The two situations are different."

"But Mollie, how are they different? In both cases you know that your client is guilty. You would mislead the court in both cases if you allowed your client to plead not guilty. How are they different?"

For the first time in five minutes Mollie Mouthpiece paused to take a breath. She slowly removed her round spectacles and cleaned them with a cloth. She blinked as she did so. Then she sternly looked at Peter Pumpkin-Eater and said in a low voice, "Peter, you are not paying me for a tutorial in 'Ethics and the Law'. You are here to seek my advice. The police have charged you with unlawfully imprisoning your wife. Now, do you wish to plead guilty or not guilty to that charge?"

As Mollie Mouthpiece spoke these words Peter Pumpkin-Eater remembered who he was and where he was. He bowed his head and softly spoke two simple words, "Not guilty."

"Excellent. We seem to be getting somewhere. Now let's see if we can find a costs agreement for your signature."

The Call Over

Peter Pumpkin-Eater sat quietly at the rear of the court.

He sat in a round wooden chair with a chocolate coloured leather cushion. Directly in front of him was a wooden banister which was also chocolate in colour. Peter Pumpkin-Eater was pleased to realise that much of the room was the colour of chocolate. His stomach rumbled when he looked at the wooden panelled walls. These resembled rich dark chocolate. He licked his lips as he observed the wooden Bar Table. This was more the colour of smooth milk chocolate. And then there was the glorious splendour of the magistrate's Bench which reminded Peter Pumpkin-Eater of a sumptuous chocolate sponge cake.

Above him, suspended tenuously from the roof, was an immense chocolate ball covered in smooth white chocolate.

Peter closed his eyes and dreamed lavish thoughts of swimming in the lush dessert of his imagination. However, his dreams vanished when he remembered where he was and why he was there.

With a start, Peter Pumpkin-Eater opened his eyes and realised that the dessert platter in front of him was crawling with ants. The ants were devouring the chocolate Bar Table! They were running around it and bustling in all directions back and forth, left and right. One of the ants had mousy blonde hair and round spectacles . . . Mollie Mouthpiece.

To one side a group of male ants, with blue bags slung over their shoulders, were talking. When Peter Pumpkin-Eater strained his ears he could hear them . . .

"How was 'The Game' on Saturday?", one ant asked poshly.

"Oh simply splendid!", another replied, "It was a wonderful match. We did rather well. Scored a thrilling try in the dying moments to win the match."

"Did Knox or Barker win?" asked a third black ant.

"Well Barker of course!" replied the second ant with more than a small degree of incredulity.

Peter wondered how an ant of that ant's age could still be playing Rugby for his school . . .

Suddenly three loud bangs echoed around the courtroom and all of the ants came to a halt. A door to the left of the Room opened and a morose man reluctantly walked to a large black leather chair at the centre of the chocolate cake and sat down. All of the ants bowed in unison. Then some of the ants sat at the milk chocolate Bar Table and others scurried to benches running along each of the two side walls and along the banister in front of Peter Pumpkin-Eater.

Magistrate Perry Pelican looked a most unhappy man. He made some notes and shuffled some papers in the silence. Then he paused . . . and decided to quickly shuffle some more papers for good measure. He slowly surveyed the scene before him, his sullen eyes dismally taking all in. Then he shuffled some more papers to make sure there were no papers which remained unshuffled. Scratching his greying beard Perry Pelican indifferently mumbled, "Right, what have you go for me? Who's first?"

Peter Pumpkin-Eater watched on as an elderly looking lawyer slowly rose to his feet and, left hand on hip, his right hand waving, impressively intoned, "Good morning Your Worship, if the court pleases I would like to mention the first matter in your charge list, the matter of Goldilocks. My name is Desmond Smith, bearister . . . I mean barrister . . . I appear for and with the defendant."

With that Desmond Smith turned and, Peter Pumpkin-Eater thought, waved to the audience. However, Peter realised that he was, in fact, motioning to a little woman in a pretty white dress to stand. She had golden locks of hair.

Mr Pelican gazed sternly in Goldilocks' general direction and murmured, "Okay Mr Smith, what's this one all about?"

"Your Worship my client is charged with break and enter."

"I see. And how does she plead?"

"Absolutely not guilty Your Worship."

"Not guilty?"

"Yes, Your Worship, one hundred per cent not guilty."

"All right." Perry Pelican shifted his sad gaze to the prosecutor who was also shuffling paper, "How many witnesses for the prosecution Sergeant Bulldog?"

"Three bears, Your Worship."

"All right", Pelican said shaking his head in time with the pages of his diary, "how's 20 July?"

"Suitable for the defendant, Your Worship."

"And for the prosecution, Your Worship."

Perry Pelican wrote in his diary and then spoke in the direction of Goldilocks, "Yes, Miss Goldilocks, come back on 20 July. Your case will be heard then. Thank you."

As Smith sat down a blob of jelly with legs shook and wiggled its way to its feet. Peter Pumpkin-Eater observed that the jelly man was the opposite of the venerable Desmond Smith. It was difficult to determine where the head stopped and the jelly man's neck began, let alone successfully identify a chin. The jelly man wobbled and fidgeted with a pen and hopped from foot to foot as he quickly said, "Ah, Your Worship, number three in, Your Worship . . . your charge list, Your Worship.

Your Worship I act for the . . . ah . . . defendant in that matter, Prince Charming . . . , Your Worship."

"And what is your name?" demanded the unhappy Mr Pelican.

"Oh . . . I'm sorry Your Worship. Pigg, Your Worship, Pigg . . . Solicitor, Your Worship."

"Is Prince Charming here?"

There was quiet laughter in the court. Peter Pumpkin-Eater laughed as it was obvious which of the observers was Prince Charming. The laughter slowly died off as a man to Peter Pumpkin-Eater's right regally rose to his feet. He was dressed in a white shirt with puffed up sleeves and a scarlet sash, black tights and shiny black boots. He quietly stood with dignity as Perry Pelican examined him and said, "Yes, Prince Charming, I see that you are here. Now, Mr . . . ah . . . Pigg, what is the position in this matter?"

"Well, Your Worship, my client is charged with sexual assault. He pleads not guilty Your Worship, not guilty."

"I see. How many witnesses Sergeant Bulldog?"

"Only the victim, Your Worship."

"Mmm. Brief to be served by 15 August Sergeant Bulldog. Committal on 30 November. Is that suitable?"

"Yes, Your Worship", Sergeant Bulldog and Mr Pigg said together.

"Thank you Gentlemen. Your Highness, I suggest you discuss this matter with Mr Pigg and he will explain to you what is happening. Thank you Sir."

For the first time the Prince spoke, "Gratitude is mine, Your Worship. I will converse with my learned counsel."

As Pigg hastily manoeuvred his way from the court with his Prince, another lawyer stood at the Bar Table, narrowly beating a further solicitor. Pelican looked in his direction and the Lawyer spoke, "Thank Your Worship, if I may mention a matter in the civil claims list, full stop, new paragraph . . . oh sorry!"

"I think you've been spending too much time with your dictaphone Mr Hedley", Pelican intoned without humour as laughter reverberated around the chocolate courtroom.

"Sorry Your Worship", continued the dictating solicitor, "Number two in the list. Humpty Dumpty and The Commonwealth. My name is Hedley and I appear for the plaintiff."

Magistrate Pelican shook his head, "Humpty Dumpty? Okay, is there any appearance for the defendant?"

"Yes Your Worship, Byrne for the first defendant."

"First defendant?" queried Pelican, "Is there a second defendant?"

"Indeed Your Worship", a third solicitor rose to his feet, "Floyd's Building Company is the second defendant. My name is Heller and I act for the Company."

"Thank you Mr Heller. Now, Mr Hedley, what is this matter about? Some sort of personal injury claim is it?"

Hedley shuffled some papers and narrated, "Yes, Your Worship. My client sues the Commonwealth for damages. He alleges that the Commonwealth was negligent in various ways. The plaintiff fell from a wall caused to be constructed by the Commonwealth. The second defendant was sub-contracted to build the wall. There are a number of particulars of negligence alleged against both defendants. Failure to warn the plaintiff as to the danger of sitting on the wall. Failure to construct a safe wall. Failure to provide a soft surface upon which members of the public, including the plaintiff, could land without injury if they fell etc."

"Significant damage?"

"Yes Your Worship. The plaintiff suffered a comminuted fracture which has severely affected his earning capacity. The plaintiff was employed as a wall-sitter Your Worship and, in addition to his physical ailments, now has a phobia of walls."

"I see. How long will the matter take to hear, Mr Hedley?"

"This will be a lengthy matter, Your Worship. Four to five weeks is the estimate."

"Four or five weeks! Why so long?"

"There are approximately five hundred witnesses, Your Worship."

"Five hundred! Who are these people?"

"All the King's Horses and all the King's Men, Your Worship."

"And how is their evidence relevant?"

"They witnessed the fall and tried to put the plaintiff back together again. They are all material witnesses Your Worship."

Magistrate Perry Pelican fell back into his leather chair and, stroking his beard, gazed towards the ceiling. He took a couple of deep breaths and then, leaning forward, spoke with a degree of menace to Messrs Bryne and Heller, "Is it possible gentlemen that you would accept a representative witness in this case?"

"A representative witness, Your Worship?" echoed Byrne and Heller.

"Yes gentlemen. Perhaps you could agree that the evidence of one of the King's Horsemen and/or one of the King's Men represent the evidence of all the King's Horsemen and all the King's Men. Is that at all possible?"

"Is it necessary Your Worship?"

"It sure would save a lot of this court's valuable time, gentlemen."

"Well . . . er . . . I could get instructions, Your Worship . . . Perhaps a short . . ."

"Make a decision!"

"We will accept a representative witness Your Worship." Byrne and Heller again spoke in unison.

"Wise decision gentlemen. I congratulate you all", intoned the magistrate, smiling for the first time, "Now, are we ready for hearing."

"Yes, Your Worship!" chorused the three lawyers.

"Excellent, how is 19 October?."

"Suitable Your Worship", said Byrne and Heller. However, Hedley hesitated and said in a barely audible voice, "Ah, Your Worship, that may not be suitable to the plaintiff."

"Why not?"

"Well, Your Worship, the plaintiff has counsel briefed in this matter. He has already had a conference with the plaintiff and has performed a good deal of work in the matter . . ."

"Mr Hedley!"

"Yes, Your Worship . . ."

"I'll give you a choice. Either I will adjourn the court for five minutes so that I can go off the Bench and obtain photocopies of cases on the subject of unavailability of counsel, or, in the alternative, you can save us all time and agree to the date now and brief new counsel. What will it be?"

"I'll take the date, Your Worship."

"Wise choice again. Good. The matter of Humpty Dumpty and the Commonwealth will be heard on 19 October. Thank you gentlemen. Now who's next?"

Peter Pumpkin-Eater's heart rose within his chest as he saw the diminutive Mollie Mouthpiece rise to her feet and address Perry Pelican.

"Your Worship, Ms Mouthpiece, Solicitor. Number seven in your charge list. The police versus Pumpkin-Eater. I appear for the defendant, Mr Pumpkin-Eater."

"Ah, Ms Mouthpiece. Good. I was hoping you would stand up next. It is the only thing that was going to stop you gossiping with the lawyers around you. Now, what is this matter about?"

"My client is charged with false imprisonment, Your Worship."

"Is your client here, Ms Mouthpiece?"

"Yes Your Worship." Mollie Mouthpiece gracefully turned so that she was facing the rear of the court and signalled to Peter Pumpkin-Eater. Peter's blood ran to his large head as he stood. He felt dizzy and had trouble focussing on the scene before him. When, at last, his eyes came into focus he saw that Magistrate Perry Pelican was glaring at him. Peter realised that he was being very closely examined. It made him feel naked.

Whereas he had had trouble hearing the words spoken previously, every syllable now echoed throughout the courtroom. He noticed that others in the court had turned to look at him. He felt tears welling up in his eyes. Finally he heard Magistrate Pelican speaking again and felt the focus leave him.

"Right, what is the plea Ms Mouthpiece?"

"I am instructed 'not guilty', Your Worship."

"All right, are you ready for hearing?"

"Yes Your Worship."

"20 October?"

"Suitable for the defendant."

"Sergeant Bulldog?"

"Suitable for the prosecution, Your Worship."

"Good. Next!"

The Plea of Guilty

"**I**s Your Worship ready to hear a short plea?"

Peter Pumpkin-Eater looked up with a start and was surprised to realise that Mollie Mouthpiece, his solicitor, was still at the Milk Chocolate Bar Table.

"The matter of the Police and Wolfe, Your Worship, number eleven in your charge list. Is Your Worship ready to hear a plea in that matter?"

Slowly Peter's brain registered that Mollie was discussing a matter other than his with Perry Pelican.

"Yes Ms Mouthpiece. I will deal with that matter now, provided that it is a short matter. Can you assure me it is short?"

"Yes Your Worship."

Peter Pumpkin-Eater's heart returned to a normal rate and he decided to remain in his seat to listen to what was to transpire.

"Thank you Your Worship, I appear for and with Mr Wolfe. As I said, this is a plea of guilty. The charge is wrongful destruction of property, to wit, a house built of hay and a house built of wood."

"Thank you Ms Mouthpiece. Sergeant Bulldog . . ."

Peter Pumpkin-Eater watched as the police prosecutor shuffled some papers and then rose tentatively to his feet. He then mumbled some words which Peter could not decipher and handed the shuffled papers to another man who, after unshuffling the papers, handed them to Perry Pelican. A lengthy silence then followed as Pelican re-shuffled the papers and then commenced reading through them.

The silence was broken by Mollie Mouthpiece who blurted out, "Oh! Your Worship! Whilst you are reading through those papers I might seek to tender three references written on behalf of my client . . ."

"It would have helped if you'd handed those papers up earlier, Ms Mouthpiece."

"My apologies Your Worship."

"Was each referee aware of the present charge when they wrote the reference Ms Mouthpiece?"

"Assuredly, Your Worship."

Silence again descended over the courtroom. All that Peter could hear was the heart of the instant defendant thumping against his hairy chest.

"Sergeant Bulldog, I note that there is a charge in addition to those Ms Mouthpiece has mentioned, a charge of attempted destruction of property . . . a brick house it seems . . . what is happening with that?"

"Withdrawn, Your Worship."

"Thank you. Now, Ms Mouthpiece, I have read the papers relevant to this matter. What would you like to say?"

"Thank you Your Worship", Mollie Mouthpiece again rose to her feet, "Mr Wolfe is 27 years old and married. He has five offspring who are dependent upon him as his wife is not employed. Mr Wolfe himself is gainfully employed as a labourer."

At this point Mollie Mouthpiece paused dramatically and turned to look briefly at her client who was quietly seated behind her before she continued, "Your Worship, as a labourer my client earns only meagre wages. He does not own his own home as he can only afford to rent small premises. Mr Wolfe, his wife and his five offspring all live in a small flat with one bedroom, a lounge room and a kitchen. The lounge room doubles for a bedroom for the offspring, Your Worship."

"Yes Miss Mouthpiece, I am sure life is quite a struggle. Move on."

"Yes Your Worship . . ." Mollie paused. "The reason for me describing my client's circumstances in such detail was to provide foundation for my next point. That is, Mr Wolfe is faced with a day to day struggle to feed his offspring, Your Worship. That brings me to the circumstances of this offence . . ."

"Thank goodness!"

"Your Worship, on the day in question my client and his family had gone without breakfast. They were starving, Your Worship, and quite desperate. It was then that my client came across the Pig brothers. He had met the brothers before, Your Worship, and had it in mind that they may have been able to provide him with food for his family. Accordingly, and quite understandably, Your Worship, Mr Wolfe approached the youngest Pig brother and politely questioned him in this regard. Upon receiving a refusal, Mr Wolfe lost his temper, Your Worship, and in sheer desperation huffed and puffed and blew the house down. It was quite unintentional Your Worship. You see, the house was a flimsy construction, being merely constructed of hay. The slightest wind and the house was flattened . . ."

"Should have made it out of wood," interjected Pelican thoughtfully. "That would have been better . . ."

"Indeed Your Worship", the pace of Mollie's speech quickened as she heard the positive note in the magistrate's voice, "it was Mr Pig's fault. How was my client to know that the foundations of the house standing before him were so unsound? If the victim had have built a stronger house this whole sorry episode would never have occurred.."

"Mmm. I see . . ."

"That is not to say that my client is innocent of the offence charged, Your Worship. He was certainly reckless as to the preservation of the first victim's house. However, the unsoundness of the first victim's dwelling clearly contributed to the extent of the damage which resulted."

"I have noted your point Ms Mouthpiece. What about the second count? What do you say about that?"

"Well, Your Worship, having met with failure with the first Pig brother, Mr Wolfe approached the second Pig brother. However, his request for food was again refused. Regretfully, Your Worship, my client again lost his temper. He was faced with a choice Your Worship. To walk away or to retaliate. Your Worship, my client made the wrong choice. He huffed again and he puffed again. And the second Pig brother's house, like that of his younger sibling, was blown down . . ."

"He should have made it of wood", Magistrate Pelican interrupted helpfully. "That would have done the trick."

"Well Your Worship," said Mollie Mouthpiece shaking her head, "sadly, the second Pig brother's house was, in fact, made of wood . . ."

"Really!", Pelican sat up straight in his chair. "Well that changes everything . . . brick? Yes, maybe brick is the answer."

Mollie Mouthpiece threw down her pen on the Bar Table dramatically and smiled a winning smile towards the magistrate, "Brick is indeed the answer, Your Worship! Your Worship mentioned a third offence earlier. That of attempting to destroy property. The subject property in that offence was the brick home of the eldest Pig brother. That house could not be dislodged Your Worship."

"Right!", Magistrate Perry Pelican grinned and hugged himself smugly before his smile quickly disappeared, "Anything further Miss Mouthpiece?"

"Yes Your Worship, I have described the circumstances of the offences . . ."

"And very well indeed, Ms Mouthpiece."

". . . and now I wish to say something about remorse. Mr Wolfe, Your Worship, is extremely sorry for what he has done. He understands that what he has done was wrong and that he must learn to control his temper. I have advised Mr Wolfe, Your Worship, that the path he is following could lead him to prison were he to re-offend. Mr Wolfe has indicated to me, Your Worship, in the strongest terms that he understands that advice and has requested that I communicate to the court his regret for these incidents. He also wishes to express his apologies to the Pig brothers. Your Worship, my client has already suffered for his actions. He has been brought before the court today which has caused him great distress and embarrassment. Furthermore, he has voluntarily agreed to assist in the reconstruction of the damaged homes and has, indeed, agreed to assist in paying for the materials required. This has, of course, greatly added to my client's financial hardship."

"Not to mention having to pay your fees, Miss Mouthpiece!"

"Yes Your Worship. Well, Your Worship, those are my submissions. I conclude by saying that I am confident that Mr Wolfe has learned his lesson and that you will not see him before this court again. Thank you Your Worship."

With that Mollie Mouthpiece sat down and like a see-saw, Peter Pumpkin-Eater observed, the defendant rose up on to his hind legs.

"Thank you Ms Mouthpiece", Perry Pelican said sternly. "Now, Mr Wolfe is there anything that you would like to say in addition to that which has been put to me by your solicitor?"

Peter heard a high-pitched whine come from the direction of Mr Wolfe and then silence.

He also wishes to express his apologies to the Pig brothers.

"I take it from your silence, Mr Wolfe, that there is nothing you wish to add", Pelican continued, "Mr Wolfe, I have carefully considered all that has been said by Ms Mouthpiece. In particular I have taken into account your financial circumstances and the pressures those circumstances have placed upon you. I have also taken into account your obvious remorse evidenced by your early plea of guilty and your willingness to assist, both physically and financially, to repairing the damage you have caused. Most importantly, Mr Wolfe, I have taken notice of the actions of the victims in this matter which contributed to the gravity of the offences. I accept the submission made by Ms Mouthpiece that had the Pig brothers constructed their homes of more durable materials the offences would have been lessened, if not avoided all together. Accordingly, whilst I consider your offences to be very serious indeed, I propose dealing with this matter pursuant to s 556A of the *Crimes Act*. In summary, I find the offences proved, but do not proceed to record convictions against you, conditional upon you entering into a bond to be of good behaviour for the period of one day."

Mollie Mouthpiece turned around in her chair and, eyes directed upwards, smiled at her client. In response, the defendant also bared his teeth. This initially caused Mollie some concern. However, she soon became accustomed to this show of affection and gave her client a playful punch to the shoulder. In return Mr Wolfe playfully bite his solicitor's nose.

When she had recovered, Mollie Mouthpiece turned again to face the magistrate.

"Now Mr Wolfe", Perry Pelican said in a deep voice, "I hope that this experience has taught you a lesson. The offences you have committed are extremely serious and, no doubt, the community would expect that I deal with you very harshly indeed, which I have attempted to do. I trust that the penalty I have imposed will cause you to think twice on the next occasion that you feel your temper rising. And as you leave this courtroom I want one thought left in your mind. That is that you will be dealt with just as harshly if not more so if you ever appear before me again. For now though, Mr Wolfe, you are excused."

As Mollie Mouthpiece left with her client, Peter Pumpkin-Eater stared into the distance and imagined what it must be like to be a magistrate. As he did so he became aware of a fly which had landed on his wrist. With a hint of optimism, Peter Pumpkin-Eater raised his hand and slapped it.

The First Barrister's Conference

Peter Pumpkin-Eater sat quietly in a waiting
room. Opposite him were a bank of elevator
doors. He peacefully observed busy looking
men scurry back and forth, in and out of doors and
up and down the stairs to this right. To his left was
a girl behind a desk. Peter was pleased by the way
she flirted with the young men who frequently
walked out of the elevator doors and up to her desk.

With alarm, Peter realised he was sinking into
the leather cushions of the lounge suite in which he
was sitting. He struggled to the surface before
starting to sink again. Peter was surprised to find
that Mollie Mouthpiece was merely perched on the
top of the cushion she was seated upon. There were
some things in life Peter could not understand.

A man calmly snored as he rested in the
lounge suite opposite Peter.

As he sipped coffee from the white cup he had
been given upon his arrival, Peter saw a sorry
looking man struggle upon crutches down a hallway
towards the elevators. As he emerged from the
darkness of the hallway, Peter realised the man's

left leg was in plaster. Beside him was a worried looking woman and behind them was a tall man with a red bushy beard. The bearded man was wearing the most extraordinary clothes Peter had ever seen. The most startling thing about his clothes was not the blue pin striped pants and the pinkish shirt but the sky blue braces with purple diamonds and matching bow tie. As the bearded man strode past the man on crutches to press the elevator button, Peter noticed that he was wearing bright red socks with white sheep.

"More like a black sheep . . .", thought Peter to himself.

The elevator doors opened and the peculiar bearded man said in a booming voice, "Well, Mr Kelly it is nice to have met you, I hope your arm gets better soon." With that the elevator doors closed and the sorry Mr Kelly and his crutches disappeared.

Suddenly, Peter Pumpkin-Eater realised that the sky blue braces were walking towards him. Mollie Mouthpiece had already risen from her seated position and was skipping towards the braces. Peter waited in his seat to see what would happen.

"Hello William", Mouthpiece chirped. "How are you?"

"Top of the world!", boomed the braces.

"Allow me to introduce Peter Pumpkin-Eater", Mollie continued, "Peter this is William Baldface, Barrister."

Peter Pumpkin-Eater struggled out of his chair and extended his hand towards the barrister's, "Good evening."

"Peter!" Billy Baldface boomed. "Welcome, walk this way."

With that, the barrister was gone. Both Peter and his solicitor trotted after him into the darkness of the hallway. They caught up with him when they found him standing in the doorway of his Chambers, arm extended, welcoming them in.

Peter Pumpkin-Eater sat in the chair to which the barrister was gesturing and Mollie Mouthpiece sat next him.

Peter was, however, immediately impressed by the barrister's immense knowledge. He obviously knew even more than Mollie Mouthpiece. There were simply rows upon rows of books running along each wall of the large barrister's room. The only place where there were no books was where there were binders bursting with loose paper. Peter Pumpkin-Eater turned to face Billy Baldface with new respect. As he examined him, Peter decided that Baldface looked like a bushranger. A rogue in any event.

"Oh Mollie, there was a call for you. Somebody from your office called to see what time you might be expected back in your office."

"Oh yes, William, that would be my secretary", Mollie smiled brightly. "You see it is my birthday today. I expect that she is making arrangements for the traditional birthday cake ceremony."

"Yes the girls here like to do that kind of thing too", Baldface said dispassionately.

Peter Pumpkin-Eater could not help but notice that the words "Happy Birthday Mollie" failed to pass the barrister's lips. To remedy this situation, Peter leaned in his solicitor's direction and whispered the customary words. Mouthpiece nodded her appreciation.

"Mollie, did I tell you about a client I saw yesterday?" Baldface's said, his level of interest in the conversation suddenly rising.

"No William, I don't think you have."

"It was a medical negligence case. The bloke said that a doctor had failed to warn him that there was a risk of gangrene setting in when they amputated his arm. I enquired as to whether he had asked whether there were any risks and he said he asked the doctor whether he could guarantee that there would be no side effects. The stupid doctor gave the guarantee. Well, I said on that evidence he had a strong case. And guess what? He tried the same thing on me. He asked whether I could guarantee that he would win his case. I said, 'Mate I'm not falling for that one'. Oh well, it worked for him once. I guess he thought he might as well give it another go!"

Peter Pumpkin-Eater sat in bewildered silence as Billy Baldface and Mollie Mouthpiece chuckled in unison. Peter noticed, however, that Mollie's chuckle was somewhat more refined than that of the barrister's.

"And I had a good win in court last week", Baldface said through grinning teeth before continuing before anybody could stop him. "Yes, it was an assault charge. You see, I was the wife. The husband's evidence was that I had him in a headlock and put my fingers in his eyes. But I managed to get in evidence of his prior conduct and the charge was thrown out." Billy Baldface paused and smiled impressively before saying limply, "It was quite a good win."

Mollie Mouthpiece smiled politely. Meanwhile Peter Pumpkin-Eater wondered how the barrister got himself into such a fight and why he was describing himself as "the wife".

"All right Mollie, what's this one about?" said Billy Baldface suddenly becoming serious.

"Well, William . . ."

"Wait! Just let me move these briefs so that I can get a better look at you", Baldface interrupted, smiling serenely.

". . . as you will see in your Brief . . .", Mollie paused as Baldface vainly started flicking through the pages in front of him, "Mr Pumpkin-Eater is charged with the offence of falsely imprisoning his wife, Mrs Pumpkin-Eater."

Peter shifted his position in his chair during the pregnant pause which enveloped the room. Finally, Billy Baldface addressed his client, "All right, Mr Pumpkin-Eater I need to give the court an explanation for your behaviour in the hope of obtaining a discount in your sentence. Could you please tell me why you imprisoned your wife."

Peter digested the words and then turned to Mollie who herself looked baffled.

"Ah, William," Mollie said softly as she leaned towards Baldface, "this is a defended matter. Mr Pumpkin-Eater has pleaded not guilty."

"Oh I see . . .", Baldface again flicked through the pages of his brief. The embarrassing silence was broken by the phone ringing.

"Hello?" Baldface swivelled in his leather bound chair to gaze out the window as he snapped up the phone, "Oh it is you. Gee! It's almost 3:00pm! I thought I might get through the day without you seeking my learned advice . . . what's that? No I've already told you. You're screwed. And when you're as screwed as much as you are you can't be unscrewed. I mean, if you had sought my advice earlier I probably could have saved you but it is too late! I think you'd better call LawCover. This is the kind of matter they should be involved in. They can appoint their own barrister to defend you. I'd like to help but I don't see how I can. It's too late . . . Okay . . . Good . . . Right . . . See you . . . Heh! Wait a second. I haven't got any briefs from you recently in those workers comp matters you were trying to round up. What you have to understand is that we don't settle any of them. We run them all! Stick with me mate and I'll make you rich! Okay. Bye."

Billy Baldface put the phone down and, after pausing to give the puzzled Pumpkin-Eater a wink, resumed his conversation with Mollie Mouthpiece, "Well, Mollie I recommend that you provide me with a statement by Mr Pumpkin-Eater, photocopies of some cases on false imprisonment and . . . ah . . . a copy of the police record. Can you help me with that?"

Mollie leaned forward in her chair, her eyebrows raised, and slowly said, "Yes I can, William. In fact, I already have. It is all in your brief."

"Right! Good! You always amaze me with your efficiency Mollie. Very impressive!"

Mollie Mouthpiece motioned for Peter to stand as she herself rose to her feet, "It's not really that impressive William. Merely sound legal practice. Like reading a brief before the man who is paying you arrives and not taking phone calls during the interview. If you would kindly return the Brief in the document exchange I would be grateful. Cheerio."

Billy Baldface did a good impression of a goldfish as Peter Pumpkin-Eater and his gallant solicitor paraded from the room.

The Second Barrister's Conference

Peter Pumpkin-Eater was delighted to see that the second barrister's room was painted the colour of pumpkin shells. This, of course, made him feel immediately at ease. He was disturbed by the absence of books but Mollie assured him that this was not a reflection on the barrister's ability to effectively present his case.

Along one wall was a series of photographs. Peter noticed that one was of the barrister holding a large fish which he had recently caught. Another showed a cricketer hitting a bouncer over the square leg fence.

As Peter sat down, Johnny Goodfellow took his position behind his large fortress of a desk and said in a resonant voice, "Welcome Mr Pumpkin-Eater. As I understand it, you are defending a charge of falsely imprisoning your wife. You deny that charge by saying that whilst she spent all of her time at home your wife was free to leave at all times. In the event that you are convicted, which I do not expect, you will lead evidence that you have no prior criminal record, have led a blameless life thus far and have already been punished in that you have effectively already lost the benefit of having a wife in that she has left you."

Goodfellow paused and looked from Pumpkin-Eater to Mouthpiece and back again.

"Is that a fair summary Mr Pumpkin-Eater?"

Peter nodded and said, "Yes Sir."

"It's a good summary thank you Jonathan", interjected Mollie.

"Splendid", Goodfellow continued melodically, his baby face shining behind square glasses. "Now, Mr Pumpkin-Eater, the way the trial will proceed is this. The prosecution will lead evidence from Mrs Pumpkin-Eater first. That evidence, I antici-pate, will be that she has spent the last so many years imprisoned in Pumpkin Shell Cottage. She will, no doubt, suggest that you have in some way compelled this situation to persist or that you have somehow prevented her from leaving."

"But there I kept her very well", Pumpkin-Eater said softly.

"I'm sure your did, I'm sure you did!" replied Goodfellow before continuing. "And I am also sure that you will do an excellent job of giving evidence to that effect."

Mollie Mouthpiece shifted her weight in her seat as she again interjected, "Will Mr Pumpkin-Eater have to give evidence Jonathan. I was hoping we could avoid that if possible."

"I agree, Mollie, I agree", Goodfellow beamed in the direction of his instructing solicitor, "I am hopeful that Mrs Pumpkin-Eater's evidence will be such that we can make a 'no case' submission at the close of her evidence."

"What does that mean?" Peter Pumpkin-Eater scratched his large head.

"Well Peter", Goodfellow gestured expansively, "if Mrs Pumpkin-Eater's evidence is not so sufficient that a court would be capable on that evidence to convict you then we can apply for your case to be dismissed before you give evidence yourself."

"But I want to give evidence. I wish to explain myself."

"I understand that Peter. However all that you may achieve is to fill in the holes in the prosecution's case. You see Peter, the onus of proof in this matter is on the prosecution. That means that they have to prove the case against you. You are entitled to be acquitted if they can not do so. The evidence they will present in an attempt to prove their case will be that of Mrs Pumpkin-Eater. If her evidence, taken at its best, is not capable of proving the case then we should make an application for the charge to be immediately dismissed. By giving evidence yourself you may very well make up for the deficiencies in their case."

"What kind of deficiencies?"

"Oh, for example, your alleged intention to deprive Mrs Pumpkin-Eater of her liberty."

"I see . . .", mumbled Pumpkin-Eater. "What if her evidence is okay?"

"Well in that case, my friend, we will have no alternative but to call you to give evidence. You will have to convince the court that your version of the events is correct and hers is not."

"But isn't that your job?"

"It is, it surely is. However, it is also yours. Peter, your solicitor and I can only do so much. And I am sure we will both do all that we are able to assist you. However, this case will turn largely on the credibility of the witnesses. That is, whether the court believes you or whether it believes Mrs Pumpkin-Eater."

"Why am I paying you so much if it is all up to me?"

"Because you need our help. What I say is true. Your evidence in this matter is vital. So is whether you are believed. However, Mollie and I are here to ensure that all the evidence that will assist you is presented to the court. That is achieved by us leading you through your evidence. Our role is also to discredit Mrs Pumpkin-Eater. She will, without question, present evidence to assist her case. Our job is to cross-examine her effectively so that that evidence is clouded at least or destroyed at best. Then, of course, there may also be questions of law which need to be argued. We are able to assist you there as well."

"Mmm."

Why am I paying you so much if it is all up to me?

Johnny Goodfellow looked towards Mollie Mouthpiece before saying, "You are, of course, free to engage other lawyers or run this matter yourself, Mr Pumpkin-Eater, if that is your desire."

Peter Pumpkin-Eater looked around the barrister's chambers and thought about what Goodfellow had said. He certainly did not fancy the idea of representing himself in court. The idea of finding a new solicitor also did not appeal to him, particularly given his soft spot for Mollie Mouthpiece. Finally he said, "No, I am happy for you to represent me."

"Good, then let's go over the evidence . . ."

Mrs Pumpkin-Eater's Evidence-in-Chief

"All right, Mr Baldface, you're for the defendant, what are your submissions in this matter?" Magistrate Perry Pelican muttered.

Peter Pumpkin-Eater sat in the back of the chocolate courtroom as the matter preceding his own was completed. He watched on as Billy Baldface, the barrister his gallant solicitor had sacked, made his submissions.

"Well ... ah ... Your Worship ... This is a matter in the Small Claims Division of this court. The plaintiff seeks damages for the damage allegedly caused to his vehicle by my client's negligent driving. The matter basically comes down to an issue as to credit. Each party gives versions of the accident which are diametrically opposed. The plaintiff says that she had a green light and my client maintains the same position."

"So why should I believe your client, Mr Baldface?"

"Well Your Worship, I believe that you are able to draw an inference as to who was most likely to run a red light from the respective driving experience of the parties . . ."

"Mmmm."

"You see Your Worship, the plaintiff is a young man, unemployed and . . . ah . . . still on his Provisional Licence. On the other hand, my client was a former driver for the Premier with twenty-five years of distinguished governmental driving service . . ."

"Mr Baldface!" Peter Pumpkin-Eater recoiled from the explosion from the chocolate cake Bench.

"Yes, Your Worship?" Baldface whimpered.

"Mr Baldface", Pelican said menacingly, "I should let you know that from my position here on the Bench I have an excellent view of the lawn outside, the oak tree and the street beyond . . ."

"Yes Your Worship?"

". . . and I was sitting here this morning during the Call Over when, as is my custom, I gazed out the window. Do you understand me?"

"No Your Worship."

"Well, I saw your client arrive in his motor vehicle," Perry Pelican leant forward in his chair so that his face was projected towards the stony faced barrister, "and do you know what I saw? Do you know what I saw? As your client attempted to reverse park his vehicle he managed not only to hit the car parked behind him but also slam into the car parked in the front. Then he got out, adjusted his glasses, and walked away as though nothing had happened. I suspect that he didn't even know."

"I see", Baldface muttered forlornly.

"But everybody on the lawn knew, Mr Baldface", Perry Pelican continued. "I saw them all standing there watching as your client performed his little trick. And do you know what is worse, Mr Baldface?"

"No."

"You were one of them!", Perry Pelican leant even closer to Baldface so that it appeared to Peter that their faces were almost touching. "You were one of those to witness the current state of your client's driving ability!"

Peter Pumpkin-Eater was intrigued by these developments. He was left feeling relieved that Baldface was not his barrister yet appalled that Pelican was going to decide his case.

"So Mr Baldface", Pelican said disdainfully as he reclined into his chair, "I think your client's case would be better advanced should you decide not to press the issue of the respective driving abilities of the parties in this matter!"

"Yes, Your Worship, perhaps that would be best."

"Yes I think so Mr Baldface."

Peter Pumpkin-Eater watched the rest of the case as it drifted to its inevitable conclusion. Finally, as Baldface crawled out of the court, Peter's case was called on for hearing.

"All right, Miss Mouthpiece, I see that you are here. Are you in this matter of Pumpkin-Eater?

"Yes Your Worship", Mollie Mouthpiece rose to her feet, "I act for Mr Pumpkin-Eater. Mr Goodfellow appears."

"Ah yes, Mr Goodfellow. It is always a pleasure to have you in my court. Now, Sergeant Bulldog, I take it you appear for the prosecution?"

"I do", barked the prosecutor.

"All right", the magistrate said as he shuffled some paper, "now this is a kidnapping charge is it not?"

"Indeed it is, Your Worship," Johnny Goodfellow spoke for the first time. "It's a charge under s 90A of the *Crimes Act*."

"And the victim is?"

"The defendant's wife, Your Worship."

"Oh I see", the Perry Pelican scratched his beard and then rubbed his bald head, "I suppose there may be some argument later as to whether a man can kidnap his own wife."

"I anticipate that that may be so, Your Worship."

"All right then", Pelican yawned, "Sergeant Bulldog, would you like to call your first witness?"

The prosecutor slowly rose to his feet and said, "Just before I do, Your Worship, an Apprehended Violence Summons was issued yesterday evening and has, I understand from my friend, been served upon the defendant. We wish that matter to be heard concurrently with this matter."

"What do you say about that Mr Goodfellow?"

"Well Your Worship", intoned the barrister. "Ordinarily I would object strenuously to such late notice. However, as the evidence in each matter is likely to be quite similar I suppose it serves no useful purpose to delay the hearing of the Apprehended Violence Summons. The defendant, with reluctance, consents to the matters being heard together."

"A wise decision, I would have thought, Mr Goodfellow."

Pelican made some notes on the court papers before looking again towards the prosecutor, "Sergeant Bulldog? Your first witness".

"Thank you Your Worship, I call the victim, Mrs Pumpkin-Eater."

Peter Pumpkin-Eater sat nervously in his chair behind and to the right of his solicitor and barrister. He looked around the courtroom and was surprised to find that the chocolate Bar Table no longer looked so appetising. Not even the sumptuous chocolate cake appealed to him any more. As he pondered on these matters he noticed, with alarm, that his wife had walked into the courtroom and was proceeding towards the witness box. Even though he knew that she would be there her presence surprised him. He felt pangs of sadness as Mrs Pumpkin-Eater glanced at him as she walked past.

"Silence in the court!"

Mrs Pumpkin-Eater stood solemnly to one side of the witness box. The court officer mumbled something to her and she pointed to the Bible. Taking the Bible in her left hand she echoed the court officer by saying, "I swear that the evidence I am about to give will be the truth, the whole truth and nothing but the truth".

"I hope she does tell the truth", Peter Pumpkin-Eater mumbled to himself.

There was a prolonged silence in the courtroom during which Peter Pumpkin-Eater looked intently at his wife whilst she looked directly out the window opposite her. Peter followed her gaze and thought about how simply marvellous it would be to be sitting on the lawn outside with the late morning sun on his face. His thoughts were interrupted by the prosecutor's abrasive voice.

"Mrs Pumpkin-Eater, could you please state your address and occupation for the record?"

Mrs Pumpkin-Eater moved her head slowly before saying in a soft voice, "I would rather not state my address but my occupation is 'home duties'".

"I'm sorry Mrs Pumpkin-Eater", Perry Pelican leant forward over the Bench. "But you will have to speak up. The microphones in front of you do not amplify your voice. They are only there to record what you say."

"I'm sorry", Mrs Pumpkin-Eater strained her voice, "I said that my occupation is 'home duties' but that I would rather not state my address."

"And why is that?" queried the prosecutor.

"I do not wish my husband to know where I live."

"I see", Bulldog continued, "now I wish to take you through the history of your marriage. When were you first married?"

"Fifteen years ago."

"And where were you married?"

"Here in Fairytown."

"Good. Now please tell the court how you would describe the first years of your marriage."

"Well", Mrs Pumpkin-Eater paused as she looked towards her husband who returned her gaze, "They were good years."

"In what way were they good?"

"My Husband", Mrs Pumpkin-Eater sobbed slightly, "Peter, that is. Peter was good to me. He was fun and caring. He used to make me pumpkin soup and bring home bunches of pumpkin leaves."

"All right. Now, when did that start to change?"

"Objection!" Goodfellow leapt to his feet.

"Yes Mr Goodfellow?" Pelican addressed the barrister.

"Sir, the question assumes that things did start to change. That is not in evidence. It is a leading question, Your Worship."

Peter Pumpkin-Eater sat forward in his chair and adjusted the neck tie which dangled below his round head. He was impressed by his barrister's gallantry.

"Sergeant Bulldog. Can you rephrase the question?"

"Yes Your Worship", Bulldog turned back to face the witness, "Mrs Pumpkin-Eater, you said a moment ago that the first years of your marriage were happy . . ."

"Yes."

". . . did things remain happy or did they change?"

"Oh! They changed."

"Okay. Now, how did they change?"

"Well, Peter stopped bringing home pumpkin leaves . . ."

"And the pumpkin soup?"

". . . I had to make that myself!"

"When did this start to happen?"

"After about the fifth year."

"All right, how did you feel at around this time?"

"I was very sad. I felt that my husband no longer loved me . . . it was not a happy time."

"Did you feel anything else?"

"In what way?"

"Well, did you feel anything in relation to your husband?"

"Oh yes! I felt that I could do better!"

"How so?"

"Well, I thought that I deserved better than what I had. I thought that my husband did not deserve me. I felt that if I left him I could find a better husband!"

These words hit Peter Pumpkin-Eater like an electric shock. Suddenly the giant chocolate courtroom began to spin. He felt small and insignificant. He wanted to leave. With a jolt Peter realised that the prosecutor and his wife were still talking.

"I see. Now Mrs Pumpkin-Eater", Bulldog was saying. "Did you attempt to leave?"

"Well, yes I did."

"What attempts did you make to leave?"

"Well I told Peter that I wanted to leave . . ."

"Mrs Pumpkin-Eater", the prosecutor interrupted. "If you're going to recount a conversation you'll have to do so in the first person. That is, 'I said', 'he said'. That kind of form. Do you understand?"

"I think so."

"Okay. Now, what was the conversation?"

"Well. I said, 'Peter, I am not happy in this marriage. I want to leave you'."

"And what did he say?"

"He said 'You can't leave. We are married and that's that!'"

"Did you have conversation to that effect more than once?"

"Oh yes. I said it to him frequently over a number of years."

"I see. Now! Did your husband physically prevent you from leaving?"

"Yes . . .", Mrs Pumpkin-Eater started crying.

"All right. How did he do this?"

For a moment all that could be heard in the courtroom was Mrs Pumpkin-Eater sobbing. Finally she began to speak, "He locked me in a room."

"He what?" exclaimed the prosecutor as if he had never heard this before, "He locked you in a room?"

"That's right. He bought a padlock and some bolts and put them on the door to my bedroom. If he went out he would force me into the room and lock me in."

"What about when your husband was at home?"

"When he was at home I was allowed to walk around freely so long as I did not try to escape."

"What happened if you tried to escape?"

"I would be locked in my room until I promised to be a good girl."

"Did your husband ever use physical force?"

"Only once."

"Only once?"

"Yes. Once I refused to go to my room when he wanted to go to work."

"What happened?"

"Well, I said I would not go and Peter grabbed hold of me and forced me into my room."

"Did he hurt you?"

"Yes, I was left with bruises on my shoulders."

"Did he hit you?"

"No."

*If he went out he would force me into the room
and lock me in.*

The prosecutor paused at this point and shuffled through his papers. Peter Pumpkin-Eater looked at Mollie Mouthpiece and took no comfort in the fact that she was not smiling. He was surprised to see, however, that Johnny Goodfellow seemed quite content.

"All right, Mrs Pumpkin-Eater", Bulldog continued, "I don't have many more questions."

"Good", Mrs Pumpkin-Eater murmured.

"Can you tell the court how you would feel about further contact with your husband?"

"I would be terrified."

"Why would you be terrified?"

"I would be afraid that I would be locked up again."

"Thank you, Mrs Pumpkin-Eater. Those are all of my questions."

Sergeant Bulldog then turned and resumed his seat behind the Bar Table. It seemed to Peter that everybody in the courtroom was taking notes except him. He also felt that his whole world had collapsed.

The Cross-Examination of Mrs Pumpkin-Eater

Peter Pumpkin-Eater sat in stony silence as his barrister rose to his feet and, after flicking through some papers, scrutinised his wife. This was a moment Peter had not been looking forward to. The delicious chocolate courtroom had been well and truly forgotten by this stage. All that Peter could think about was the fact that his life was falling apart, and how sad it was that this should occur in public ... in this drab little room where "justice" was exercised.

"Mrs Pumpkin-Eater", Johnny Goodfellow smiled, "If you have no objection I would like to go over some of the evidence you just gave."

"Okay", Peter heard his wife reply.

"You don't mind if we do that do you?"

"No ... not at all."

Peter was relieved to hear the assuring tones in his barrister's voice. He had hoped, of course, that his wife would not be tortured upon the witness stand. He certainly did not want that.

"Good", the barrister continued. "Now let me get this right. Did I understand your evidence correctly when you said that your husband had been good to you in the early years of your marriage?"

"That's correct."

"He made pumpkin soup for you and brought home bunches of pumpkin leaves, did he not?"

"He did."

"And I take it that the bunches of pumpkin leaves were by way of a present, correct?"

"Yes, he liked to surprise me with a gift when he got home from work."

"I see. So you had no complaints in those early years?"

"No more than any wife."

"Sure. But all in all Peter was a good husband to you?"

"In those early years, yes."

"But then you started wishing for more in life."

Peter Pumpkin-Eater noticed a hint of menace in Goodfellow's voice as he asked this question. He looked to his wife to see if she had noticed it. It appeared that she had not.

"Yes. As I said earlier, I wondered whether I couldn't find a better husband if I left Peter."

"So you were dissatisfied."

"Yes."

"Despite the pumpkin soup and the bunches of pumpkin leaves you were dissatisfied."

"Well . . ."

"You were dissatisfied!"

". . . Peter had stopped bringing those things home."

"I see."

Johnny Goodfellow stopped and poured himself a glass of water from the carafe on the Bar Table. Peter held his large head in his hands whilst Perry Pelican gazed off into the distance. Mrs Pumpkin-Eater looked furtively around the courtroom.

"Mrs Pumpkin-Eater", the kindness in Goodfellow's voice had returned, "at the risk of offending you, I wish to put a proposition to you. Would that be all right?"

"Yes."

"Splendid", Goodfellow rocked on to the heels of his feet. "What I wish to put to you is this. Would it be possible that Peter ceased to cook you pumpkin soup or bring home bunches of pumpkin leaves because . . . how should I put this . . . you had . . . let me see . . . failed . . . in your duties as a wife?"

"What?"

"I am simply suggesting to you that Peter's behaviour may have been caused by your own failure. That is, your failure, over time, as a wife. Would that be possible?"

Mrs Pumpkin-Eater sat up straight in her chair in obvious shock. For a moment or two she found it hard to speak. However, she finally blurted out, "No! I do not think that is possible!"

"Mrs Pumpkin-Eater", said Goodfellow reassuringly, "I do not mean to cause any offence. However, as you know marriage is a two way street. Is it not at least possible that Peter withdrew his favours due to your failure to reciprocate?"

"Objection!" barked the prosecutor. "The witness has already answered that question."

"With respect to my friend, Your Worship", said Goodfellow, "the question is different. I asked earlier whether she had failed to be a good wife and was met with an absolute denial. I am now asking whether it was at least possible that she had failed in this manner. They are different questions, Your Worship."

"I agree with Mr Goodfellow, Sergeant Bulldog", Perry Pelican yawned. "I will allow the question."

"As Your Worship pleases", the prosecutor grumbled.

"Mrs Pumpkin-Eater", Goodfellow addressed the witness, "do you recall the question?"

"I do."

"Would you care to answer it?"

"No. It is not possible that I failed in my duties as a wife."

"Not at all possible?"

"No."

"I see", Goodfellow paused and read through some of his notes. "All right. Now! Mrs Pumpkin-Eater you said in your evidence, did you not, that you felt that you 'deserved better' in life than being married to the defendant?"

"Yes."

"Those aren't your exact words but they are the effect of what you said, correct?"

"Yes, I wanted better in life."

"But you not only wanted better, did you? You thought you deserved better, right?"

Mrs Pumpkin-Eater stopped and thought and then said defiantly, "Yes! I felt that I deserved better."

"You deserved better because you were a good person."

"That's right!"

"And what's more, a good woman."

"Yes!"

"And this pipsqueak of a husband was beneath you."

"Yeah!"

"So you decided you wanted to leave."

"That's right!"

"And you decided to cease being a good wife to your husband because he wasn't a good husband to you."

"Absolutely!"

Peter Pumpkin-Eater, who until this stage had been horrified by the direction that the questioning was taking, slumped into his chair and almost smiled. Mrs Pumpkin-Eater suddenly realised what she had said and let out a hint of an anguished cry. Mollie Mouthpiece smiled serenely to herself. Meanwhile, the Melancholy Magistrate yawned.

Johnny Goodfellow waited until he thought sufficient time had elapsed to allow Mrs Pumpkin-

Eater's words to sink in before stating, "So! You did withdraw your spousal services after all!"

"But not until Peter had withdrawn his!" Mrs Pumpkin-Eater retorted with equal belligerence. Peter Pumpkin-Eater observed that these words stunned his brave counsel. Even Mollie put her hand to her head before she regained control. However, Goodfellow quickly recomposed himself and asked, "But is not this a chicken and egg argument, Mrs Pumpkin-Eater?"

"What do you mean?"

"Quite simply this. You say that Peter ceased to be a good husband first. I say that you ceased to be a good wife first. How is the court to know which occurred first?"

"I don't know."

"Then is it not fair to say, Mrs Pumpkin-Eater, that the situation was, at least, that both you and your husband allowed the marriage to break down?"

"Yes, I suppose that is true."

"It was not then solely my client's fault."

"No."

"You were yourself at least partially to blame."

"Yes."

"All right. We seem to be getting somewhere", Goodfellow took a sip from his glass of water before theatrically pausing to think. "Now, Mrs Pumpkin-Eater you said earlier when my friend was questioning you that you confronted the defendant on a number of occasions and requested that he allow you to leave the marriage, correct?"

"Yes, I did so over a number of years."

"Well I put it to you that you never made any such request."

"But I did", Mrs Pumpkin-Eater looked around the courtroom confused.

"I put it to you Mrs Pumpkin-Eater that you did not once discuss the possibility of leaving the marriage with the defendant."

"I did discuss it."

"I see."

Johnny Goodfellow turned to look towards Mollie Mouthpiece who nodded and pushed a piece of paper in his direction.

"You also said, Mrs Pumpkin-Eater", Goodfellow continued, "that Peter physically locked you in your room to prevent you from leaving the house."

"That's right."

"Well that's a baldfaced lie isn't it!" Goodfellow raised his voice and, simultaneously stamped his foot.

"No! It is true", Mrs Pumpkin-Eater said, her voice wavering.

"I put it to you that he did no such thing!"

"He did!"

"I put it to you that you were free to leave the house at all times."

"That is not so."

"I see", Goodfellow stood up straight and, his bottom lip trembling, gazed blankly at the Bar Table. He then slowly reached forward and grasped the carafe of water. He carefully picked up his glass and proceeded to pour the water from the carafe to the glass. He then placed the glass of water on the Bar Table and raised the almost full carafe to his lips and commenced to drink from it.

"Thirsty are you Mr Goodfellow?", chuckled Perry Pelican.

"Oh, I'm sorry Your Worship", Goodfellow laughed, "I shouldn't try and do two things at once, I was too busy thinking."

"Well I realise that takes all of your cranial capacity Mr Goodfellow."

All of the courtroom exploded into laughter, including Peter Pumpkin-Eater. Mollie Mouthpiece was positively doubled up with mirth. Even Mrs Pumpkin-Eater chuckled.

Finally, Goodfellow continued, "My apologies, Mrs Pumpkin-Eater. I trust that your concentration was not disturbed."

"No, I'm fine", Mrs Pumpkin-Eater responded to Goodfellow's warmth with sullenness.

"Good. Now Mrs Pumpkin-Eater, there is one aspect of your evidence which, frankly, confuses me."

"Yes."

"You maintain that your earlier evidence that Mr Pumpkin-Eater prevented you from leaving the house by locking you in your room is the truth, correct?"

"Yes, he did."

"However, I recall you saying earlier that Peter only used physical force once."

"Yes."

"Is that correct?"

"It is."

"Over what period are we talking, Mrs Pumpkin-Eater? When do you say Peter first started locking you up?"

"Around three to four years ago."

"I see. So your evidence, Mrs Pumpkin-Eater, is that my client successfully imprisoned you in your room over a period of three to four years though only using physical force once. Is that your evidence?"

"Yes."

"But Mrs Pumpkin-Eater! How can this be so? How on earth did Peter compel you to go into your room without using physical force."

"You weren't there Mr Goodfellow. He's a very persuasive man."

"Mrs Pumpkin-Eater", Goodfellow said in soothing tones, "I put it to you that this entire case is based upon falsehoods. I suggest that Peter did not imprison you without physical force because he, in fact, never imprisoned you. Isn't that the case?"

"No."

"I have nothing further for this witness, Your Worship."

"Thank you, Mr Goodfellow", mumbled the magistrate. "Any re-examination Sergeant Bulldog?"

"No, Your Worship", came the bark.

"Excellent!"

The "No Case" Submission

Peter Pumpkin-Eater felt his heart sinking to the bottom of his stomach. He realised that it would soon be his turn to stand, walk around the chocolate Bar Table and sit in the electric witness box. Peter felt no other emotion than pure dread.

It was therefore with more than a little relief that Peter Pumpkin-Eater saw his barrister, after a lengthy discussion with the sweet Mollie Mouthpiece, rise again to his feet and state simply, "Your Worship, the Defence has a submission to make at this stage of these proceedings."

Peter was not encouraged, however by the look of shock on Perry Pelican's face. Nor by the manner in which the Bulldog's head whipped around to face Goodfellow.

When Pelican had regained his speech he said, "I take it Mr Goodfellow, that the submission you wish to make is a 'no case' submission. Is that right?"

"That is correct", Goodfellow said smugly.

"All right then, I will be intrigued to hear it", the Melancholy Magistrate smirked as he rested back in his leather chair.

"Thank you Your Worship. It is trite for me to say that the prosecution has an onus of proof in matters of this nature to present evidence which is capable of satisfying Your Worship, beyond reasonable doubt, that the defendant is guilty of the offence charged. That is, they must prove each element of the offence beyond reasonable doubt. But I am sure that all of that is familiar to Your Worship."

"Yes, I have heard it said before", Pelican laughed.

"The defendant's respectful submission, Your Worship", Goodfellow carefully weighed his words, "is that the prosecution have failed to present sufficient evidence to be capable of satisfying Your Worship of the 'intention' element. That is, an intention to deprive Mrs Pumpkin-Eater of her liberty."

"Mm. I see", Pelican looked suddenly serious.

"Your Worship has heard evidence from Mrs Pumpkin-Eater that she was locked in her room by the defendant. Even if Your Worship were to accept that evidence, which we do not concede, there is no evidence as to the means used by the defendant to compel Mrs Pumpkin-Eater to enter the room. Indeed, Mrs Pumpkin-Eater's evidence, I think, was that only once over a period of three or four years did the defendant use physical force.

Which begs the obvious question, Your Worship, how on earth did the defendant compel her to enter? No evidence was led in this regard Your Worship. There is simply no evidence to show that Mrs Pumpkin-Eater did anything other than enter the room of her own free will."

"An interesting argument Mr Goodfellow."

"Now Your Worship", Goodfellow again adopted his soothing voice, "you can only allow this matter to proceed if you find that the prosecution's evidence is capable of satisfying you beyond reasonable doubt that my client intended to deprive Mrs Pumpkin-Eater of her liberty. My submission is that, even taken at its highest, the prosecution is not capable of so satisfying you. If you are with me Your Worship then you must discharge the defendant immediately and not put him through the horrors of cross-examination. That is my submission Your Worship."

"Thank you, Mr Goodfellow. Sergeant Bulldog? Anything in reply?"

Peter Pumpkin-Eater held his breath. The idea of not being subjected to the horrors of cross-examination appealed to him.

"Yes, Your Worship", grumbled the prosecutor, "I won't take up much of your time. Regardless of how the defendant compelled the victim to enter the room, the uncontested evidence is that the defendant locked her in. My argument is that you are able to infer from the act of locking the bedroom door that the defendant intended to deprive the victim of her liberty. How she got there is not relevant. Simple as that, Your Worship."

Peter recommenced his normal breathing pattern. Even he saw the strength in the prosecutor's words.

"Mm, very interesting", Pelican mused. "I must say that the defendant's argument interests me. The deficiency in the evidence as to how the defendant forced Mrs Pumpkin-Eater into the room without using physical force does worry me. However, the prosecutor's argument in connection with the act of locking the door is, obviously I think, compelling. I find that the evidence of the defendant locking the door is capable of satisfying me that the defendant intended to deprive Mrs Pumpkin-Eater of her liberty. In any event, I am anxious to hear what the defendant has to say in this matter."

Peter Pumpkin-Eater bowed his head.

"Now, Mr Pumpkin-Eater, my ruling does not mean that I have found you guilty of the offence. All that my ruling means is that the evidence I have heard thus far is capable of proving your guilt. Now, it may well be that your evidence will convince me otherwise. That is yet to be seen. Do you follow?"

Peter Pumpkin-Eater mumbled that unfortunately he did.

The Start of Peter Pumpkin-Eater's Evidence-in-Chief

Peter Pumpkin-Eater knew that his time had come. Although he did not actually hear the words, he understood that he had been directed to stand and walk towards the witness box. As he stood, he felt as if he was towering over the Bar Table and those sitting around it. He wished that his presence was not so damned obvious. He carefully put his left foot forward and commenced to walk in slow motion around the Bar Table. As he drew level with it, and the faces of his legal representatives came into view, Peter could see that Goodfellow was engrossed in the papers in his brief whereas Mollie was smiling encouragingly towards him. Bulldog was positively scowling. Finally, Peter reached the witness box. The next thing he knew he was half way through his oath and was being directed to sit in the box. Peter Pumpkin-Eater sat looking in the direction of Perry Pelican until his barrister demanded his attention.

"Mr Pumpkin-Eater, could you please state your address and occupation for the record?"

Peter cocked his head to one side and tried to digest the meaning of the words that he had heard. He opened his mouth and, after a pause, he said, "Oh, my address is 'Pumpkin Shell Cottage', Fairytown. I am a pumpkin distributor."

"And you are the defendant in these proceedings?"

"The defendant . . . ? Oh yes, I'm the defendant."

"Good! Now Mr Pumpkin-Eater you have been sitting in the court this morning and you have heard all the evidence, correct?"

"Ah, yes. That's right."

"Excellent. Now you have heard your wife give evidence about your marriage . . ."

"Yes."

". . . and you heard her state that your marriage began to break down after about five years."

"Yes, I heard her say that."

"Good. Now what can you tell the court about the breakdown of your marriage?"

Peter Pumpkin-Eater gazed out over the courtroom. He was surprised how different it looked from his new vantage point. He struggled to focus his eyes on Mollie Mouthpiece who appeared to have an expressionless look on her face. Peter wondered why she was not smiling, or at least frowning . . . something. To his left Peter saw the magistrate above him. It occurred to Peter that Pelican appeared to be entirely ignorant of his presence. He certainly didn't look in his direction.

Peter wondered why that was . . . And then to his right, sitting behind the menacing Sergeant Bulldog, was his sombre wife . . .

"Mr Pumpkin-Eater, do you wish me to repeat the question?"

Peter Pumpkin-Eater was jolted out of his dream." Oh! I'm sorry! What did you say?", Peter said in a daze.

"Mr Pumpkin-Eater, I simply asked you to describe to the court your version of how the marriage broke down."

"Oh, certainly . . . yes", Peter's mind snapped into focus. "After about five or six years, my wife stopped showing me any kind of affection whatsoever. I don't know why. It really did happen very suddenly. But I don't know what caused my wife to behave that way."

"Had you withdrawn any of your services at that stage?"

"Not at all! I was still bringing bunches of pumpkin leaves home. And I was still making pumpkin soup for her. But for some reason, my wife stopped doing all the things she used to do."

"And you have no idea why?"

"No. None."

"All right, so what did you do?"

"Well, initially I continued to make pumpkin soup and bring home pumpkin leaves . . ."

"For how long?"

"A matter of months. Perhaps three or four months."

"Go on."

"Okay. As I said I continued to do all the usual things. But my wife didn't return any kind of affection whatsoever. I asked her what was wrong but she would not tell me."

"So what effect did all of this have upon your marriage?"

"Well, it ruined it. I couldn't keep the marriage going by myself. I needed her help. But she was not prepared to help."

"All right, so you do not dispute, do you, that the marriage broke down?"

"No", Peter said sadly, "I don't dispute that."

Goodfellow again paused to confer with his brief before continuing, "And you have no idea why the marriage broke down other than that your wife inexplicably withdrew?"

"No."

"No reason comes to mind at all?"

Peter Pumpkin-Eater stared at his barrister and then bowed his head and gazed at his round shoes. Finally, he looked up and said very slowly and so softly that even Perry Pelican strained to hear, "Well, actually there is one thing that comes to mind."

"Oh? And what would that be?" Johnny Goodfellow asked uncertainly.

Suddenly it seemed to Peter that every neck in the courtroom had extended in his direction and every head had grown to the size of a large pumpkin and was cocked to one side waiting for him to answer.

"Well ... I found out that my wife ... Mrs Pumpkin-Eater ... was having ... an affair!"

"What!" Chorused each person in the courtroom including the Melancholy Magistrate who suddenly, it seemed, was taking an interest in the hearing unfolding before him.

"What did you say Peter? What was it you said?" Goodfellow urged.

"I said ...", Peter Pumpkin looked painfully towards his wife who, for the first time, engaged eye contact with him.

"Yes, Peter ..."

Peter looked uncertainly towards the barrister who was talking to him and then straightened in the witness box defiantly, "I said that my wife was having an affair and that is why she withdrew her services as a wife!"

"With whom?"

Peter looked again towards his wife who now had tears dancing down her cheeks and said, "Marty the Milkman!"

"Objection, Your Worship, objection!" the prosecutor finally interjected.

"Yes, Sergeant Bulldog? You have an objection, do you?" Pelican said with a hint of mirth.

"Yes, Your Worship. None of this was put to Mrs Pumpkin-Eater. I object to all of the evidence relating to this alleged affair on the basis of *Browne v Dunn*, Your Worship. It's all inadmissible."

"Mr Goodfellow?"

Marty the Milkman!

"Your Worship", Goodfellow said carefully, "I would appreciate the opportunity to obtain instructions from my client in this matter. Perhaps a short adjournment?"

"I will adjourn the court for fifteen minutes."

"All rise!"

The Short Adjournment

As soon as Peter Pumpkin-Eater shuffled onto the verandah of the court he immediately became aware of the anger being directed towards him.

"Why on earth did you not tell me?" growled Goodfellow.

"Tell you what?"

"About Marty the Milkman!"

"I didn't think it was relevant . . ."

Goodfellow bowed his head and took a couple of deep breaths. Mollie Mouthpiece glided over to Peter and put her hand on his shoulder before walking on. Goodfellow raised his head and attempted to smile in Peter's direction before saying, "Listen Peter, let me explain something. Perhaps I should have explained it to you before . . ."

Goodfellow's voice trailed off before he continued, "When you are on trial, your entire life is on trial. Particularly in matters like this which involve a marriage. Nothing is irrelevant! And not just your life. Oh no! Not just your life!"

Goodfellow paused dramatically before pointing into the courtroom.

"Her life is on trial too! The victim's life. Everything which may assist the court in understanding what may or may not have happened is relevant. I mean ... you don't think the court strictly applies the elements of the offence, do you? No Sir! The magistrate will weigh all that has happened and apportion blame. Oh yes, he'll couch his decision in terms of the elements of the offence. But in the end he'll only find you guilty if he thinks you deserve to be found guilty ..."

"And he may not think I deserve it if my wife has cheated on me ..."

"That's right!"

"So everything's all right, isn't it? I told him about the affair."

"No, you didn't."

"What do you mean I didn't? I just said it!"

Goodfellow chuckled to himself and waved his instructing solicitor over, "Mollie, explain *Browne v Dunn* to our client."

Johnny Goodfellow strode off to walk along the verandah. Both Peter Pumpkin-Eater and Mollie Mouthpiece watched him leave before Mollie said soothingly, "Peter, *Browne v Dunn* is a legal case which basically says that if you have an allegation to make it must be put to the witness whilst they are on the witness stand. You have to give them a chance to answer the allegation ... to explain themselves."

Peter's eyes darted about. He was confused.

"You see, Peter", Mollie continued, "we didn't raise the affair with your wife when Mr Goodfellow was cross-examining her. It's only come up in your evidence. Mrs Pumpkin-Eater has not been given the opportunity to say that she was not having an affair . . ."

"But she was!"

". . . I know. The problem is, Peter, that the court will not view it as being fair to allow your allegation to stand when your wife has not been given the opportunity to refute it."

"So what happens now?"

"Well", Mollie Mouthpiece grimaced. "The magistrate will not allow your evidence of the affair into evidence."

"What does that mean?"

"It means that he will not consider it when he makes his decision."

"But he's already heard it! How can he ignore it now?"

"Well, magistrates are very talented people, Peter", Mollie said sarcastically, "they have the ability to divide their minds into two. All the evidence goes in one side but only the admissible evidence goes out the other side."

"Oh God . . ."

Peter Pumpkin-Eater stood silently with his solicitor. He looked over the lawn which was golden with late morning sunlight. The large oak tree which sat in the middle of the lawn bristled with the breeze and whispered the secrets of thousands of privileged solicitor/client discussions it had heard over countless years.

Peter was still dreaming when Goodfellow returned.

"So how are we going?" Goodfellow asked.

"I've explained *Browne v Dunn*, Jonathan."

"Splendid", Goodfellow joined the silence.

"Why did you ask me?" Peter Pumpkin-Eater finally whispered.

"Ask you what, Peter?"

"Why did you ask me about the affair if the magistrate wouldn't allow me to talk about it?"

"Well, you see Peter, I didn't know about the affair. You hadn't told me about it before. Quick. Let's go back into court and get this matter over with."

"The sooner the better", Peter mumbled as he shuffled back into the courtroom.

"But before we do ..." Goodfellow stopped suddenly. "Is there anything else you haven't told me? You don't have any more surprises do you, Peter?"

"No", Peter replied sadly.

The Conclusion of Peter Pumpkin-Eater's Evidence-in-Chief

"**A**ll right Gentlemen, are we ready to continue with this matter of Pumpkin-Eater?"

"Yes, Your Worship", Goodfellow stood up, "Your Worship, immediately prior to the adjournment my friend had objected to certain evidence my client had led in connection with an alleged affair enjoyed by his wife."

"That's right, Your Worship", Bulldog barked.

"Well, Mr Goodfellow I don't perceive much room for you to move here."

"No, Your Worship. The law appears reasonably settled in this area."

"Good", Pelican sighed, "I rule then that any evidence adduced by the defendant as to the alleged affair is inadmissible."

"As Your Worship pleases."

Perry Pelican nodded to Goodfellow and then shuffled some papers in a satisfied manner.

"Mr Goodfellow, do you wish to continue examining the defendant?"

"Thank you, Your Worship."

"Now Mr Pumpkin-Eater", the magistrate leaned towards the witness, "you understand, don't you, that you are still under oath?"

"Yes Sir."

"Good. Please continue Mr Goodfellow."

"Mr Pumpkin-Eater", Goodfellow directed his attention to his client, "I won't keep you much longer."

"Mm."

"I wish to address this issue that you imprisoned your wife."

"Okay."

"Well, you heard your wife's evidence, did you not?"

"I did."

"And you heard her say that over a period of years you locked her in a bedroom when you went out?"

"Yes."

"What do you say about that evidence."

"It is entirely false!"

"Entirely false. Good. And you also heard her say, did you not, that she was allowed to roam freely when you were home but was forced back into her bedroom when you went out."

"Yes."

"What is your reaction to that evidence?"

"It is untrue!"

"Splendid. Now Mr Pumpkin-Eater, I want you to listen to these questions very carefully."

"Okay."

"Did you ever lock your wife in her bedroom?"

"No."

"Did you lock her in any room whatsoever."

"I did not."

"Did you ever prevent her from leaving 'Pumpkin Shell Cottage'?"

"Never!"

"Mr Pumpkin-Eater, has your wife any reason to fear that you would ever lock her in her room?

"No!"

"Thank you, Your Worship, I have no further questions."

Peter Pumpkin-Eater looked at Mollie Mouthpiece and was pleased that she was smiling.

The Cross-Examination of Peter Pumpkin-Eater

"**M**r Pumpkin-Eater", Bulldog snarled, "you're another wife-beating husband, aren't you?"

Peter Pumpkin-Eater was immediately repelled by the prosecutor's unrestrained hostility.

"Your Worship! I must object!" Goodfellow was on his feet. "There is absolutely no evidence to suggest the defendant has beaten his wife. In fact, the victim denies it!"

"I withdraw it, Your Worship", Bulldog grumbled. "Sir, I put it to you that you're just another little man who treats his wife like dirt!"

"Your Worship!", Goodfellow was back on his feet. "The prosecutor is fighting with the witness not cross-examining him."

"Try and calm down, Sergeant Bulldog", Pelican said indifferently.

"All right ... Mr Pumpkin-Eater, you locked your wife in her room didn't you?"

"No ...", Peter gulped, "I didn't ... I didn't do that."

"Well, you've heard you wife say that you did!'

"Yes."

"She said it here no more than an hour ago!"

"Mm."

"Well, why would she say you did if you didn't?"

"I don't know."

"She said it because you did do it, didn't you?"

"I didn't."

"Are you sure of that?"

"Of course I am! I didn't do it!"

"Well", the prosecutor paused, "I put it to you that you did!"

"I object Your Worship", Goodfellow rose again to his feet with serene calmness.

"Yes, Mr Goodfellow", Pelican slowly allowed his head to pivot so that it faced Pumpkin-Eater's barrister.

"Your Worship, my learned friend . . ."

"I'm not your friend!" snarled Bulldog with unrestrained venom.

"And neither, Sir, are you learned", Johnny Goodfellow whispered in the prosecutor's general direction. "But that is just another legal nicety which has no doubt escaped your understanding."

"What . . . ?"

"Gentlemen!" Perry Pelican interjected, "please at least pretend to be civil."

"My apology, Your Worship!" Goodfellow intoned whilst Bulldog permitted himself to grumble.

"Thank you. Now, Mr Goodfellow . . . you were saying?"

"Yes, Your Worship. I was saying that my learned friend is quarrelling with the witness. He has asked him the same question, albeit in differing forms, a number of times and has received the same answer. It is clear, however, that my friend is not satisfied with the answer that he has been given and has persisted with the matter. His line of questioning is clearly objectionable."

"Yes, Mr Goodfellow", the magistrate yawned once again, "Sergeant Bulldog kindly move on to a new topic."

"Fine . . ."

Peter Pumpkin-Eater paused to wonder whether the prosecutor was actually angry with him or just pretending to be.

"Mr Pumpkin-Eater", Bulldog drew Peter back into the action, "you have said in your evidence that you did not prevent your wife from leaving the house. Is that right?"

"Yes."

"You did not prevent her from leaving?"

"No."

"Is that your evidence?"

"Yes."

"You expect this court to believe that you did not prevent or attempt to prevent your wife from leaving 'Pumpkin Shell Cottage'?"

"Yes, because it is true!"

"You're not serious!"

"Your Worship!" Goodfellow again calmly interjected.

"Yes, Mr Goodfellow, you can sit back down", Perry Pelican waved lazily towards the barrister, "Sergeant Bulldog, you are harassing the witness. If you can't think of any other line of questioning please stop now and I will give my judgement."

"I have more questions, Your Worship. I haven't finished yet."

"Please get on with it", the Melancholy Magistrate implored with complete disinterest.

Peter Pumpkin-Eater quickly took a deep breath to stop his head from spinning. He just finished doing so before the petulant prosecutor's next barrage commenced.

"Sir, I put it to you that you were an inadequate husband."

"What?" Peter exclaimed.

"I suggest, Mr Pumpkin-Eater, that you were not a good husband. I put it to you that you were not able to meet your wife's needs."

Peter Pumpkin-Eater sat in the witness chair in silence. As he did so he realised that he must look a pathetic figure to those in the courtroom. His eyes drifted towards his wife who stared back expressionlessly in his direction. Suddenly Peter felt an overwhelming sadness envelope him. He wondered how his marriage could have fallen apart so badly that it had to be defiled here in a court-room . . . in public.

"Please answer the question", mumbled the magistrate who had neither sympathy nor interest in the state of Peter's marriage. Peter realised that the magistrate had probably seen it all before.

"I was a good husband", Peter replied in a voice that, though inextricably soft, echoed strangely around the room.

"A good husband!" the prosecutor cruelly mocked. "How can you say you were a good husband when your wife is here in court accusing you of imprisoning her in her own house? How can you say it?"

Peter thought for a while and then said in carefully measured words, "I believe I was a good husband. I believe that the marriage failed, and we are here today, because my wife was not able to give me the commitment that the marriage required to survive because . . ."

"Oh come on Mr Pumpkin-Eater!"

". . . because my wife was in love with Marty the Milkman."

Peter Pumpkin-Eater fell back into the witness chair in forlorn resignation. He knew his marriage was now no more than a rumour. It was over. He forced his mouth tightly closed and, though he wanted to, he forced himself to avoid glancing in the direction of his wife.

"All right, Mr Pumpkin-Eater", Bulldog broke the silence, "as you have raised Marty the Milkman again how about we address that issue . . ."

Mollie Mouthpiece's mouth dropped open as the full effect of the prosecutor's words sunk in. Her mousy hair flapped against her round face as she turned her head to look at Johnny Goodfellow who was equally stunned. Mollie strained her neck and, putting her lips to the barrister's ear, whispered, "He's opened the door hasn't he? He can't complain about the question not being put to the victim if he chooses to raise it, right?"

Johnny Goodfellow nodded quickly.

"I put it to you that this entire Marty the Milkman fairytale is a fabrication!" Bulldog continued.

"It is not", Peter shook his head.

"It is a cliche Mr Pumpkin-Eater. No man's wife runs off with the milkman. It just doesn't happen."

"She did."

"I put it to you Mr Pumpkin-Eater, that you have manufactured this allegation with the sole purpose of ridiculing your wife."

"No."

"And to divert attention from your crime."

"I did not."

"Yes, you did!"

"No, I didn't."

The petulant prosecutor huffed and then looked down towards the papers on the Bar Table. He muttered to himself before looking up again towards Peter Pumpkin-Eater.

"Mr Pumpkin-Eater, am I correct in saying that your evidence is that you never imprisoned your wife . . . ?"

"That's right."

". . . and your wife has no grounds to fear of you doing so in the future?"

"Yes."

"Then answer this question Mr Pumpkin-Eater", Bulldog snarled, "if your evidence is the truth, why has your wife made these allegations against you?"

"Because she wants a reason to end our marriage so that she will be free to marry Marty."

"Oh I see", Bulldog mumbled before turning to the Melancholy Magistrate and grumbling, "nothing further for this witness, Your Worship."

For the first time the hint of a smile crossed Peter Pumpkin-Eater's lips.

The Submissions and the Verdict

Peter Pumpkin-Eater retreated to the comfort of his chair behind his legal representatives. He sat quietly and tried not to think about his predicament.

A thunderous silence descended across the courtroom. Perry Pelican again commenced his paper shuffling ritual. Bulldog sat forward aggressively in his chair and, with intent, caused grievous bodily harm to a fly which had the temerity to crawl across the Bar Table in front of him. Meanwhile, Mollie Mouthpiece played with her pen as she sat perched on her chair. Johnny Goodfellow lounged elegantly beside her.

Finally, the Melancholy Magistrate muttered morosely and the petulant prosecutor rose to this feet and commenced his submissions.

"Your Worship, I will be brief. You have heard all the evidence . . ."

"Yes I have", Pelican interjected with self-assessed mirth.

". . . and you will have noticed that the evidence of the defendant and his victim are different. It is a matter for you Your Worship. The question is who you believe. If you believe the victim's evidence you will convict the defendant. I say that you should believe her evidence. It was evidence that was easily believable. There was nothing far fetched about it. She gave her evidence in a straightforward manner without exaggeration. Her evidence, Your Worship, should be preferred over that of the defendant. I say that you should find that the matter has been proved beyond a reasonable doubt and you should convict the defendant."

The prosecutor resumed his seat in a flurry and resumed his search for errant insects on his Bar Table.

"Thank you, Sergeant Bulldog", Pelican glanced at his watch. "Mr Goodfellow?"

"Thank you indeed, Your Worship", Goodfellow intoned. "This is, as my friend has stated, a case in which the evidence of the two key players was diametrically opposed. Mrs Pumpkin-Eater says that she was imprisoned within her home. She says that she was locked within her room and prevented from leaving. On the other hand, Mr Pumpkin-Eater denies that he ever resisted his wife's leaving of the home. He did so in the simplest of terms and with considerable conviction. Now Your Worship, there is no denying that the marriage in this matter broke down. Neither party denies that.

"The alleged victim says that the marriage broke down because Mr Pumpkin-Eater failed to

That makes it admissible.

provide marital services whereas Mr Pumpkin-Eater's evidence is that the marriage was destroyed by his wife's infidelity with Marty the Milkman . . ."

"I object!" the prosecutor snapped. "*Browne v Dunn*. None of this was put to the victim when she was giving evidence."

"I'm afraid that you raised it in the defendant's cross-examination, my friend. That makes it admissible", Goodfellow retorted.

"He's right Sergeant Bulldog", Pelican murmured. "You raised it. There's nothing improper in Mr Goodfellow relying upon that evidence."

"Mm, I see."

"Please continue Mr Goodfellow."

"Thank you, Your Worship. I was just saying, prior to my friend's objection . . ."

"We're not friends . . ."

". . . that my client's evidence was that the marriage broke down due to his wife's affair with the milkman, Marty the Milkman."

Goodfellow paused to ensure that the magistrate fully digested the effect of his words.

"Now Your Worship", Goodfellow continued, "to convict Mr Pumpkin-Eater today of the offence of kidnapping you must be satisfied that he in fact detained his wife and that he intended to do so. You must be satisfied of each of those elements beyond a reasonable doubt. Both elements beyond a reasonable doubt, Your Worship."

Goodfellow again paused whilst the magistrate showed every sign of ignoring his theatrics.

"My submission Your Worship is that neither element has been proved. As to the element of in fact detaining the victim, I would submit, with respect Your Worship, that the alleged victim's bald statement that she was detained is not sufficient to prove the fact. Mrs Pumpkin-Eater says she was detained and Mr Pumpkin-Eater denies it. I submit that you cannot be satisfied beyond a reasonable doubt on that evidence."

"Mmm", Perry Pelican responded to Goodfellow's submissions, "and the second element?"

"Well Your Worship, it is my submission, as I stated during my 'no case' submission, that the prosecution has failed to adduce any evidence to show that the defendant intended to detain his wife. However, I concede that Your Worship did not find favour with the argument I advanced on that occasion and the same, no doubt, still applies. In fairness, Your Worship, given your earlier ruling, I feel compelled to concede that intention must necessarily be proved by the prosecution if Your Worship is satisfied that my client in fact locked his wife in her room and prevented her from leaving the house. Accordingly, Your Worship, this case simply turns upon whether you are satisfied of that fact."

"That is a fair assessment of the case", Perry Pelican stated encouragingly.

"Thank you, Your Worship. Now, on the evidence my respectful submission is that you should find the following history. The parties were married; the marriage broke down; the marriage broke down predominantly due to the wife's affair with the milkman; the wife wishes to leave the marriage and the wife has fabricated this complaint against her husband. You should find Your Worship, on the evidence, that Mr Pumpkin-Eater did not imprison, detain or kidnap his wife. In the event that Your Worship is with me, then it naturally follows that the Apprehended Violence Summons should also be dismissed. Thank you Your Worship, those are my submissions."

Johnny Goodfellow fell back gracefully into his seat. Mollie Mouthpiece nodded and both lawyers turned to look at Peter Pumpkin-Eater. Peter attempted to smile but was not able to. His attention was distracted by a fly crawling across his wrist.

"Please stand Mr Pumpkin-Eater", Perry Pelican said without looking towards the defendant.

Peter Pumpkin-Eater followed the magistrate's direction. Once again he stood naked before Lady Justice. He strained to hear the words falling from the Melancholy Magistrate's lips, words that would affect the rest of his life . . .

"This is the matter of Peter Pumpkin-Eater. The defendant is charged with kidnapping his wife. I have heard the evidence. I have a doubt. The defendant is discharged. Thank you, gentlemen. This court is adjourned for lunch."

With that Perry Pelican rose to his feet and with surprising speed strode from the courtroom and was gone.

Peter heard his wife cry as Mollie Mouthpiece turned to him and shook his hand.

"Congratulations Peter, you've won!"

The Aftermath

"**W**ell, I don't believe in aftermaths so I'll be on my way", Goodfellow said expansively. "Congratulations Mr Pumpkin-Eater. It was nice to meet you. All the best. Cheerio!"

Johnny Goodfellow heaved his blue barrister's bag over his shoulder and strode off.

Peter Pumpkin-Eater, still stunned, watched him leave. A thousand questions were running through his mind. However, none of them reached his mouth.

"Well, how about that?" Mollie Mouthpiece punched her client's arm as her eyes beamed from behind her round spectacles. "You must be delighted! Must be a relief?"

"Yes, I suppose it is."

"You 'suppose' it is. Aren't you sure?"

"My marriage is over Ms Mouthpiece. I didn't realise how much she wanted it over."

"Yes I see. I'm sorry", Mollie Mouthpiece's enthusiasm dried up.

For a few moments the solicitor and her client stood together in silence on the verandah of Fairytown Local Court. Peter looked over the grass lawn which appeared strangely different to the way he recalled it that morning, a hundred years ago. Finally Peter Pumpkin-Eater spoke.

"I couldn't keep her, you know?"

"I'm sorry Peter. What was that?"

"I had a wife but I couldn't keep her."

"But what could you do?"

"I kept her in 'Pumpkin Shell Cottage'."

"You what?"

"I kept her in 'Pumpkin Shell Cottage' . . . but there I kept her very well."

Mollie Mouthpiece stood staring at her client in stunned silence as Peter Pumpkin-Eater's words trailed off sadly. A single tear made its way slowly down Peter's cheek.

"I kept her there very well . . . but now she's gone", Peter whispered before turning to Mollie Mouthpiece and saying with half a smile, "Thank you Mollie for your help. I'll leave you alone."

With that Peter Pumpkin-Eater shuffled away from the chocolate court house and the scene of his perverse downfall. He knew nothing would ever be the same again.

Meanwhile, Mollie Mouthpiece remained on the court's verandah. She stood straight-backed with her feet together and her guilty client's file clutched to her breast. She wondered whether Peter Pumpkin-Eater's sentence was sufficient.

STUDENTS' GUIDE TO
LEGAL WRITING

Enid Campbell, Richard Fox, Gretchen Kewley

Students' Guide to Legal Writing provides all you need to know about presentation and preparation of law papers. It gives practical advice on how to prepare written work and quality research. Whether writing an essay or a thesis, the guide outlines matters of style, referencing and citation, information on library strategies, and further recommended reading. It is invaluable for any student of law or legal studies.

1997 • 1 86287 277 5• 64 pp • $10.00